FAMOUS
MEN AND WOMEN

The story of
Joan of Arc

...iring stories of great men
... women, specially told
for children

OTHER TITLES IN
THE JUNIOR CHILDREN'S LIBRARY

Robin Hood

Sinbad

Aladdin

Uncle Tom's Cabin

Little Women

Each book is illustrated with pictures suitable
for colouring with crayons, pencils or paints.

Published by Brown Watson (Leicester) Ltd.,
55a London Road, Leicester LE2 OPE.
Printed in Hungary.

The Story of
JOAN OF ARC

(With Pictures for Colouring)

In the year 1412 a baby girl was born in the little French village of Domremy. Her father's name was Jacques D'Arc and the baby was given the name Joan at her baptism in the tiny village church.

Joan's parents were hard-working peasant farmers. They had to labour long hours in the fields, tilling their few acres of land, in order to grow enough food for the family. Joan grew up to be a rather serious child, with a solemn expression, very seldom brightened by a smile. For all that, her manner was pleasant and appealing, and never was her voice heard raised in anger.

From an early age, Joan became aware that all was not well with the fair land of France. One evening while still very young she happened to see her mother crying bitterly in the kitchen.

"Papa," she asked, "why does Mama weep?"

"Because she has just heard, my daughter, that her sister's son has been killed in the war." For a moment Joan looked very puzzled.

3

"Papa, what is this 'war' you speak of?"

"Ah, my child, when two countries cannot agree, and send men to fight against one another, that is what we call war. Now the war in which your cousin was killed has raged for the last eighty years between ourselves and the English. The English want to rule France and have sent huge armies to conquer us. Now we have just been defeated in a terrible battle at Agincourt, and soon all France will be in the hands of our enemies."

Joan was very sad to hear of the plight of her native land.

"But, father, what about our own soldiers? I am sure they are every bit as good as the English, why can't they save us?"

"Alas, Joan, our leaders are weak and cowardly, and care only for their own safety and comfort, while the enemy is bravely led by King Henry of England, who is a fine soldier and a great leader. If only we had a king like him, we would soon drive the English out of France. Now, Joan, that's your history lesson for to-day, so off you go to the kitchen and help your mother with the washing."

"Papa, what is this 'war' you speak of?"

Joan Grows Up

The years passed and Joan still lived the normal life of any French peasant girl. She helped her mother around the house, washing, baking bread and spinning cloth from wool. She assisted her father as well, by looking after their few sheep and goats, and sometimes when her father was busy elsewhere, she even followed the plough.

She was very devout, said her prayers every day, and attended church with great devotion each Sunday. When there was any sickness in the little village, Joan was always on hand.

Of course it was not by any means a case of all work and no play, for Joan loved to join in fun and games with the other young girls of the village.

Throughout these years France kept up the unequal struggle with England. Old King Charles VI had died, leaving a son known as the Dauphin, who was both foolish and cowardly. He had fled to hiding in the town of Poitiers. King Henry of England had married a French princess and the old Queen of France betrayed her country by agreeing to let Henry's infant son be the next King of France. If this were allowed to happen France would be ruled by an English King.

When father was busy, Joan even followed the plough.

Strange Voices

One evening when she was about thirteen years old, Joan was working in the fields near her house. Suddenly she heard a voice coming as it were from heaven.

"I am the Archangel Michael," it said. "I come to tell you that a great task lies ahead of you."

Then the voice stopped, and Joan stood there gazing in wonder towards heaven.

"Oh, I must have been dreaming," she said to herself, "perhaps I have been working too hard. I shall sit down and take a rest."

But Joan had not been dreaming, for in the years that followed the voices spoke to her again and again. Sometimes it was St. Michael, at other times St. Margaret or St. Catherine.

Joan told nobody about the voices and so far the voices themselves had given her no definite instructions as to how she was to set about her great task.

At last in 1428, the voices told her exactly what she was to do.

"You must go to Robert de Baudricourt and ask him to bring you to the Dauphin. The Dauphin will give you command of his army.   You will raise the siege of Orleans, and you will have the Dauphin crowned as King of France at Rheims."

CAN YOU ANSWER THESE QUESTIONS?

Where and in what year was Joan of Arc born?

How did Joan help her father and mother?

Who was ruler of France at this time?

What king led the English army against France?

What heavenly voice first told Joan that she would help her country get its freedom?

What other heavenly voices spoke to Joan?

What did the heavenly voice tell Joan to do?

Her Work Begins

With her childlike faith, Joan did not doubt for one moment, that she would do all her Voices had instructed. "Perhaps I should tell Mama why I am going to see Robert de Baudricourt," she mused. "No, better not, for she would probably scold me for having such silly ideas. I shall tell Uncle instead, for he is kind and understanding and he knows the man I want to see."

So she sought out her uncle and told him what she had in mind.

His eyes opened wide in amazement.

"I know nothing of your voices," he replied, "but I do know my friend Robert de Baudricourt, and I can guess the answer he will give when you tell him what you want."

"Uncle, let me worry about that. All you have to do is bring me to your friend. After that my Voices will look after me."

"All right, Joan, you will have your way, but don't tell me later that I did not warn you."

When Robert heard what Joan had in mind he roared with laughter. "Laxart," he said, "I gave you credit for more intelligence than to come wasting my precious time in this fashion.

Joan told her uncle about her "Voices".

Take this young girl home and tell her father to give her a good whipping. Perhaps that will help to remove her silly notions."

But Joan made her Uncle return with her again and again to de Baudricourt. On her last visit she was shown into the council chamber where a meeting of the council was in session. She walked boldly up to where Robert was sitting.

"I come to make a last plea for your help," she said. "The position is now desperate, for our army has just been defeated in a great battle near Orleans."

Robert sprang to his feet.

"How could you know this?" he demanded, "for it would take days for the news to arrive here."

"My Voices have told me," Joan replied quietly. "If what you say proves to be true," said Robert, "I will do what you ask."

When news of the defeat was brought by a messenger two days afterwards, Robert gave Joan a troop of horsemen to guide her to the Dauphin.

CAN YOU ANSWER THESE QUESTIONS?

To whom did Joan go for help?
What did Robert de Baudricourt say to Joan?
Why did he finally agree to help her?

"How can you know this?" he demanded.

Joan Meets the Dauphin

Joan disguised herself as a peasant, and jumping on her horse, rode off with her escort. It was an eleven days' journey to the town of Chinon, where the Dauphin now had his court.

Every mile of the way was beset with danger, for bands of English soldiers roamed the countryside, pillaging and looting. They had also heard that Joan was on the road to Chinon, and were keeping a sharp watchout for her.

"If we can capture her," they said to one another, "we will be well rewarded by our general."

But Joan and her escort avoided all danger and at last arrived safely in Chinon.

The townsfolk had advance news of her arrival and came out in their hundreds to cheer her as she rode by.

"Long live Joan, long live the maid," they shouted. "France will soon be free."

Joan rode straight to the Dauphin's court, and demanded an audience. The courtiers tried to trick her, by pretending that one or other of them was the Dauphin but each time Joan saw through their trickery.

"Have done with this foolery," she cried, "and

Joan rode off with her escort.

take me at once to the Dauphin, for whom I have an important message."

But the Dauphin made one excuse after another.

"I am too tired to-day," he would say, or "to-day I have to go hunting. Tell her to come back to-morrow."

"Tell the Dauphin that I shall give him the answer to the secret question that troubles his mind," said Joan.

The Dauphin was very impressed when he received this message and he sent for Joan at once.

"Who are you?" he demanded, "and why do pester me like this?"

"I am Joan of Arc," she replied "and the Lord has told me to have you crowned King of France. You are also to give me command of your army, and with it I will raise the siege of Orleans."

The Dauphin listened until Joan had finished, and then bent down and whispered in her ear.

"Now, my child, what is the secret that troubles me?"

"You are worried because you are wondering if you are really the true heir to the throne of France. Well, you can set your mind at ease, for the Lord has told me that you and only you are the heir to the throne."

"The Lord has told me to have you crowned King."

Joan Has Her Way

The Dauphin was now convinced that Joan was telling the truth, but it was not so easy to persuade his councillors, who were jealous of her.

They questioned her for many days, and at last it was agreed by all that she was a good Christian and that the Dauphin would be well advised to be guided by her. Thereupon the Dauphin announced that Joan was to be given command of the French Army and at once many noblemen and thousands of troops flocked to her standard. The townspeople presented Joan herself with a magnificent suit of armour and a beautiful white horse.

The wonderful confidence she inspired in her troops was truly miraculous. Her influence was felt in other ways too, for the soldiers no longer swore and got drunk as before.

Within a few weeks, Joan set out at the head of her army for Orleans. The English had built many strong forts on all the roads leading to the city, and Joan's advisers felt that it would be madness to try and break through them. "I am commander-in-chief of the army," she said in reply to their objections. "Follow me and all will be well."

Joan rode on a beautiful white horse.

One of the old French generals disobeyed her orders, and led part of the army in another direction. In spite of this Joan persisted with her own plan, broke through the line of forts, and succeeded in relieving Orleans.

When the English general saw he had been outsmarted he was furious. "Attack in force at once," he ordered, "and let's show the French and that peasant maid of theirs how the English can fight."

All to no avail however, for Joan's troops were already marching to attack the largest of the English forts, which they captured after a long and bitter struggle. Throughout the battle, Joan stayed at the head of the army, encouraging and urging on her men to greater efforts. Relentlessly they drove the English before them, shouting their war cry, 'For France and Joan'.

When all the forts had been captured, the army marched back in triumph to Orleans, where Joan was given a heroine's welcome.

CAN YOU ANSWER THESE QUESTIONS?

What convinced the Dauphin that Joan was telling the truth?

What city did Joan win from the English?

What was the war cry of Joan's army?

"Attack in force at once," the English general ordered.

A King is Crowned

Joan had accomplished the first part of her task. Now she had to persuade the Dauphin to come to Rheims to be crowned King of France.

"You have done well, Joan," he said, "and your reward shall be great. Ask what you will and it is yours."

"I want only this, your Majesty," she replied, "that you come to Rheims at once and be crowned. My army will give you all the protection you need on your journey."

"But that is impossible, Joan, for the English hold most of the countryside between Chinon and Rheims. We would all be killed, of that I am certain."

"Very well, your Majesty. My army will clear the way for you, so that you will have no excuse left."

Joan was as good as her word, and in a few weeks defeated the English in a series of great battles. In the last battle at Patay, the enemy were utterly routed, and the way to Rheims lay open.

The Dauphin was crowned amid great pomp and ceremony. Joan was very happy, for so far she had succeeded in doing all the Voices told her to do. All that now remained was to drive the remnants of the English army out of France forever.

But alas, she failed to do this, for the new King was lazy and hesitant, and refused to listen to her advice.

"We have lots of time, Joan," he said, "why not rest after your campaigns, and later we will discuss ways and means to drive out the English."

"But, your Majesty," pleaded Joan, "now is the time, while they are still confused and scattered. If we allow them to re-organise their armies and rebuild their forts, all our work will be undone."

But the King was unyielding. Instead he yielded to other advice and tried to make peace with the English. Finally Joan was betrayed and handed over to the enemy.

CAN YOU ANSWER THESE QUESTIONS?

How did Joan persuade the Dauphin to go to Rheims to be crowned king?

Where did Joan gain a great victory for the French army?

Was the Dauphin crowned King of France?

Why did Joan fail to drive the remnants of the English army out of France?

A Noble Death

Joan was thrown into prison where she lay for weeks in chains, before she was brought to trial before fifty judges. A man called Cauchon conducted the trial against her, and he tried to prove that she was a witch and that she was guilty of heresy.

"Now, Joan," he began, "we have all heard so much about these wonderful Voices of yours. Perhaps you would tell the court exactly what they said to you."

"My Voices have forbidden me to speak of them to anyone but the King himself," she bravely replied.

She was led down to the torture chamber in the prison vaults and shown the rack. "If you do not answer, your body will be tortured on the rack," they said to her. "Were you to tear me limb from limb, I will tell you nothing more," was her reply.

After two trials the judges were unable to trick her into admitting that she had done wrong, for this simple young girl proved just as clever as the learned men who questioned her.

At last, worn out by the hardships of prison

"I shall tell the King only," said Joan.

life and the cruel endless questioning of her persecutors, Joan signed a paper without knowing what it contained. What she had signed was a confession that she was a heretic, and it proved to be her own death warrant.

On May 30th, 1431, she was led through the streets of Rouen to the market square, where she was to be burned at the stake.

When she saw the stake she shuddered and cried out: "I would rather be beheaded seven times than burned." But her Voices spoke to her again, telling her to be patient and resigned, for soon she would be in heaven.

When the fire was lit she called out for a cross, and a priest thrust a cross mounted on a staff into her hands. As the flames rose around her, her lips were seen to move in silent prayer, while she clasped the cross to her breast.

So died in her twentieth year one of the greatest heroines of all time. But her life did not end in defeat, for her cruel death so enraged the people of France that they rose in their thousands and drove the English invader out of France forever.

Joan's name was also honoured, for the Church in 1456 declared that all the charges against her were false and in 1919 she was proclaimed a Saint.

As the flames rose around her, her lips moved in prayer.

FAMOUS
MEN AND WOMEN

The story of

Boadicea

**Inspiring stories of great men
and women, specially told
for children**

The Story of
BOADICEA

(With pictures for Colouring)

Long, long ago, when the Romans first came to Britain, there lived a beautiful young princess called Boadicea. Her father was King of the Britons in the part that we now call Norfolk and Suffolk. That meant he was ruler of the North Folk and the South Folk. At this time Princess Boadicea was about seven years of age, and all the people loved her.

We know very little about Britain in those days, almost two thousand years ago. Our own history was only just beginning, and the greatest nation then was known as the Roman Empire. The Romans were fine soldiers and they were very clever at building, and left us many towns and great long roads.

The Chariot Race

At first the Britons fought fiercely against the Roman soldiers. They charged upon the Romans in chariots that sent the invaders flying. These chariots had sharp knives fixed to their wooden wheels, which made each speeding chariot a deadly weapon. But after many battles the Britons allowed the Romans to settle, and for some time there was peace.

As Princess Boadicea grew up she loved to play with boys rather than girls of her own age. She did not bother with indoor pastimes like sewing, or decking herself out in fine necklaces, brooches and rings. When the boys had a mock battle or boar-hunt she would join in, often as leader of the winning side.

In a nearby Roman camp there was a boy of about sixteen named Mark Augustus. He was inclined to boast and swagger, most of all when riding in a chariot, snapping his whip over the horses. Princess Boadicea one day challenged Mark to race his chariot against hers.

"Done!" shouted Mark. "We'll race along this road my father built. Just watch me win, you silly girl!"

When the boys had a boar-hunt she would join in the game.

Princess Boadicea looked very tall and proud in her chariot drawn by two splendid horses. She was determined to teach the vain Mark a lesson. As crowds gathered to see the race the two chariots lined up, and at the signal to go, thundered off in a cloud of dust.

Mark drew slightly ahead. Then they were racing neck and neck—nearer and nearer an old oak-tree which was the winning post. Mark lashed his horses, but Boadicea did not use a whip. "Faster! Faster!" she cried to her horses and with a mighty effort they drew level, and flashed past the oak-tree well in front of the astonished Mark!

Boadicea's Marriage

Boadicea's father was now growing old, and before he died he appointed a brave chieftain named Alun to be King. In those days the ruler had to be a soldier who could lead his people in battle. But the new King was unhappy. He was deeply in love with the beautiful Princess Boadicea. At last she consented to be his wife.

There was a splendid wedding-feast in the camp on a hill where the Britons lived. Bonfires blazed. There were singers there and Druids in their white

"Faster! Faster!" she cried to her horses.

habits. And among the guests invited by Boadicea was the young Roman soldier, Mark Augustus.

Now Mark had never forgiven Boadicea for having beaten him in the chariot race. In fact he had vowed to get his revenge in some way, even if it were years later. So Mark Augustus made a surly-looking guest, for he did not like to see the lovely Princess laughing and gay.

"Just wait!" he muttered, clenching his fists. "I shall be made Governor of Britain yet. I shall have power over this King and his Princess. Then we shall see who will win!"

Without knowing it, Princess Boadicea had made herself a dangerous and bitter enemy. And as Mark Augustus grew older he became even more ambitious. At last his dream came true. A letter was brought from Rome, from the Emperor Claudius, making Mark Augustus Governor of Britain!

CAN YOU ANSWER THESE QUESTIONS?

What powerful army invaded Britain when Queen Boadicea was a little girl?

What famous Roman did Princess Boadicea challenge to a chariot race?

What king married Princess Boadicea?

What appointment did Mark Augustus receive from the Emperor Claudius?

Among the guests was Mark Augustus.

The Roman Governor's Revenge

Britain was now at peace, and Britons and Romans lived and worked together as good friends. But this did not suit the plans of the new Governor. In his boastful and high-handed way he began to enforce laws which made the Kings of Britain angry.

Fighting broke out again, and one of the warlike Britons named Caractacus was taken prisoner and sent to Rome with his wife and children. In another battle, King Alun, husband of Boadicea, was wounded and was brought home dying. "My dearest wife Boadicea," said the King, "I wish you to be the leader of my people. When I am gone, you shall be Queen."

When the Roman Governor heard of this, he laughed. The moment had come for his revenge. In future there would be no Kings or Queens in Britain, and no ruler except the Roman Governor. Britain must lie under the rulership of Rome!

Boadicea was very angry when she was told about this new law. Most of the Roman laws were just and good, and indeed our own laws to-day are based upon those Roman laws of long ago. But this latest order struck at freedom itself—

"When I am gone, you shall be Queen."

and freedom has always been the very life of Britons.

What the young Queen did not guess was that the Governor was filled with petty spite against her! So she walked into a carefully-laid trap. She went to see the Governor, feeling sure he would listen to reason and see that justice was done.

At last, having waited for a long time outside the Roman Court of Judgment, the tall and beautiful Queen Boadicea was permitted to enter. And there, on the judgment chair, sat Mark Augustus.

"I have a complaint, which I ask you to hear," said the Queen. "Your laws cannot be obeyed by Britons."

"Indeed," said the Governor, smiling. "Why so?"

"Because they are unjust!" cried Boadicea. "Your new law would take away my kingdom. That is not fair. We have our own customs and we should be left free to follow them."

"Ah, proud lady. You forget that Britain is now conquered, and is part of the Roman Empire."

"Your laws cannot be obeyed by Britons."

"We shall never be conquered!" Boadicea drew herself upright, hands clenched, eyes flashing fire. "We shall never be slaves!"

The Governor shrugged. He beckoned two soldiers to advance beside Boadicea.

" Have this woman removed," he said calmly, "and publicly beaten with rods. That will teach her to obey!"

CAN YOU ANSWER THESE QUESTIONS?

Why did the Kings of Britain become angry with Mark Augustus?

What happened to Queen Boadicea's husband?

Why did Queen Boadicea visit the Governor?

What did the Queen say to the Governor?

What was Mark Augustus' reply to the Queen?

"Have this woman removed," the Governor said.

Queen Boadicea goes to War

The Roman Governor had made a great mistake in thinking that Boadicea would humbly submit to his power. She had good reason to hate the Romans, for they had proved themselves not only unjust but cruel. She vowed that the grass would be red with Roman blood, and every Roman in Britain be driven into the sea!

The Queen called her people together. She stood on a hill-top in their midst looking very lovely in a long robe and with a gold chain about her waist. When she called upon them to march with her against the Roman invaders the crowd roared approval.

Like wildfire the word spread. That very night a great army had gathered around the Queen's palace, their spears glinting in the moonlight. These Britons loved their beautiful Queen, and very soon the Romans learned to fear her.

As dawn broke, the great forests awoke to a cheer. With chariots thundering, Boadicea and her terrible horde descended upon the nearest Roman stronghold. They battered in the gates. They swept into the town and drove out every Roman, leaving the town in flames.

The Queen called her people together.

So it went on week after week, and as Boadicea's army marched it grew, as more and more recruits fell into line. The Queen's heart leaped with a sudden resolve. In the midst of her warriors, a hundred thousand men, she gazed about her with flashing eyes at the thick forest of spears.

"Well done, Britons!" she cried. "And now must come the final test. March on!" From her chariot the Queen swept one hand forward while the other gripped the reins. "On, my soldiers—to Londinium!"

Londinium! That was the greatest Roman stronghold, where the large city of London now stands. Even at that time it was a great fortified town. From its protecting walls the Roman general, Seutonius, saw that the approaching Britons far outnumbered his own men. He ordered his army to march out of Londinium.

Alas, this was only a trick. For when Boadicea's warriors poured into the town the Roman army suddenly came back. But the Queen was ready for them.

"Fight like men!" she commanded. "Rather than be taken prisoner, I would gladly die!"

There followed a terrible battle. The Roman

"On, my soldiers, to Londinium," she shouted.

soldiers were outnumbered, but they were all trained men. By standing together and obeying the orders of their general, the Roman legions won the day.

Queen Boadicea was true to her word, and at the last moment she drank poison. She died that day, in the year A.D. 62, that Britain might be free. And eighty-thousand Britons died for the same cause around the chariot of Queen Boadicea.

For this reason we remember with pride the name of Britain's first Queen, after almost two thousand years.

The End

CAN YOU ANSWER THESE QUESTIONS ?

What did Queen Boadicea order the people to do?

In what place did they attack the Romans?

What did the Roman general command his army to do?

Which side was victorious in this battle?

How did Queen Boadicea die?

What year did she die?

Queen Boadicea died that day that Britain might be free.